THE MICROWAVE
Shakespeare

Other titles in the series

A MIDSUMMER NIGHT'S DREAM

Rans☙m

A Midsummer Night's Dream
Published by Ransom Publishing Ltd.
Unit 7, Brocklands Farm, West Meon, Hampshire GU32 1JN, UK
www.ransom.co.uk

ISBN   978 178591 337 2
First published in 2019

CONTENTS

WHERE

The events of the play take place in two locations: the city of **Athens**, in Greece, and a forest not far from Athens.

Parts of the play also take place in **Fairy Land**, which overlaps with the above two places.

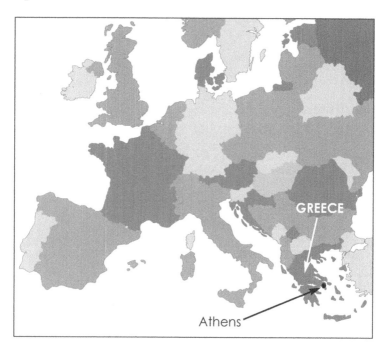

WHEN

It's not at all clear when the action in the play takes place. Shakespeare probably set the events of the play to be in *his* 'present' – that is, about the time that the play was written.

The play itself was probably written in about 1595 or 1596.

HELPFUL NOTE

All the spoken words in this book that are in italics, *'like this'*, are actual words taken from Shakespeare's play. They are spoken by one of the actors in the play.

WHO

Theseus – Duke of Athens
Hippolyta – Queen of the Amazons

Theseus   Hippolyta   Hermia

Hermia – daughter of Egeus, betrothed to Demetrius
Egeus – father to Hermia

Demetrius – betrothed to Hermia

Lysander – in love with Hermia

Helena – in love with Demetrius

Lysander   Helena   Demetrius

Philostrate – master of the revels to
Theseus

Oberon – King of the Fairies
Titania – Queen of the Fairies

Puck – a fairy, or sprite (he also goes by the name of **Robin Goodfellow**)

Oberon　　　Titania　　　Puck

Quince – a carpenter
Bottom – a weaver
Flute – a bellows-mender
Snout – a tinker
Snug – a joiner
Starveling – a tailor

The Globe Theatre. Above is a reconstruction of the original Globe Theatre, which is in London. Below is a cross-section of the original theatre, which was built in 1599.

Shakespeare's plays were performed at this theatre. When you read this book, just imagine standing in the crowd, in front of this stage, watching the play.

ONE

Theseus, Duke of Athens, is in his palace. He's with **Hippolyta, Queen of the Amazons**. He's going to marry her in just four days time – and he can't wait! OK, it's true that he met her on the battlefield – and he *did* injure her:

'*Hippolyta, I woo'd thee with my sword,*
And won thy love, doing thee injuries.'

But now it's different: they are in love.

Theseus sends his master of the revels, **Philostrate**, off to get the young people of Athens ready to party.

Then **Egeus** comes in with his daughter, **Hermia**, and two other men: **Demetrius** and **Lysander**.

Egeus is angry. In fact, he's furious. He explains to Theseus that Demetrius has agreed to marry Hermia – he's already got Egeus's permission and it's all been arranged. But now this Lysander person has come along and stolen Hermia's heart.

'This man hath bewitch'd the bosom of my child,' says Egeus, 'by giving her poems and little presents, and by singing fake love songs to her under her window by moonlight.'

Lysander, says Egeus, has:

'Turn'd her obedience, which is due to me,
To stubborn harshness.'

Egeus tells them all that, since Hermia won't obey him, then according to the ancient law of Athens he can either *make* her marry Demetrius – or he can have her killed.

Theseus really doesn't need all this hassle. He's got a wedding to look forward to.

'OK, Hermia,' he says to her, 'what have you got to say? You should obey your father. He should be like a god to you – after all, he gave you your beauty. And besides, *Demetrius is a worthy gentleman.'*

'*So is Lysander*,' says Hermia. Straight back at you!

('Going well,' thinks Theseus.)

'But your father doesn't like Lysander!' says Theseus. 'And *your eyes must with his judgment look.'*

'OK,' Hermia says. 'Just tell me. What's the worst that can happen to me if I refuse to marry Demetrius?'

'Well, either you'll be executed – or you'll never see a man ever again. You'll become a nun and never know what it is to love a man.' Even with his wedding in four days time, Theseus is losing the will to live.

'That's fine by me!' says Hermia. 'It'll definitely be better than marrying Demetrius!'

'Right. You have until my wedding day to make up your mind,' replies Theseus. 'Death, Demetrius or a nunnery. Your call. Think about it, Hermia.'

'Sweet Hermia,' Demetrius begs. 'Give it up! Lysander, tell her to marry me!'

Lysander just laughs. 'Egeus loves you, Demetrius, so why don't you marry *him*?'

'She is mine,' Egeus butts in. 'I'm her father, so I'll decide who she marries!'

'Look,' Lysander tells Theseus, 'I am just as good as Demetrius in every way. Plus, I love her more than he does, which is most important of all. And anyway, Demetrius used to run after **Helena**, and he made her fall in love with him. He's a cheater!'

'Oh yes,' Theseus remembers. 'I was going to talk to him about that. Egeus and Demetrius – come with me! We need to have a few words. Now, Hermia, say "Yes" to Demetrius – or else! Come with us, Hippolyta!'

They all go out, leaving Lysander and Hermia alone together.

'*The course of true love never did run smooth*,' says Lysander, trying to cheer Hermia up. 'Either lovers are not the same rank in life and can't marry, or one is young and the other is old, or other people control who they can love. And even if the lovers are a good match, then war, death or sickness can ruin their love,

Making it momentary as a sound,
Swift as a shadow, short as any dream;
Brief as the lightning in the collied night.'

'We just need to be patient,' replies Hermia (patiently).

'Anyhow,' Lysander continues, 'I have an aunt who lives a fair way outside Athens. She hasn't got any children, so she has given me all her love. We could get married there, where the strict laws of Athens can't get us. So if you love me, meet me tomorrow night in that wood where we met up with Helena in May. I'll wait there for you.'

'Oh Lysander! I promise I'll be there!'

'Shh! Here comes Helena!'

'Hi, *fair Helena*, where are you off to?' Hermia says casually.

'Did you call me *fair*?' Helena asks angrily. 'Take it back. You're the fair one, according to Demetrius. He thinks you are beautiful. Sickness is catching; I wish beauty was catching too. I'd give up everything – except Demetrius – to catch your beauty.'

Obviously Helena's still got the hots for Demetrius.

'Well, I don't give Demetrius any

encouragement,' answers Hermia. '*I frown
upon him, yet he loves me still ... I give him
curses, yet he gives me love ... The more I
hate, the more he follows me.*'

'It's all your beauty's fault!' says Helena,
bitterly.

So Hermia decides to tell Helena their
plans, to calm her down. With Hermia
gone, surely daft Demetrius will love Helena
again! 'Don't worry, Helena, he won't see
my face again,' she says. 'Lysander and I

plan to run away tomorrow. We are going to meet up in that wood where you and I used to chat and tell each other secrets. Then we'll be gone and you'll have Demetrius all to yourself.'

She turns to her lover. 'Lysander, I'll see you tomorrow, at midnight in the wood.'

Lysander and Hermia both depart, leaving Helena alone.

'Why does Demetrius love Hermia?' Helena wonders bitterly. 'I am just as beautiful as her. He used to love me. I know! I'll tell him what Lysander and Hermia are planning to do. He may thank me for the information – and anyway, at least I'll get to see him again.'

Off she goes to find Demetrius!

'Is all our company here?'

In a small house in Athens, some workmen are meeting up. There is **Bottom**, the weaver, **Flute**, who mends bellows, **Starveling**, the tailor, and **Snout** who mends pots and pans. Then there is **Snug**, a joiner, and **Quince**, a carpenter. They are at Quince's home.

They are going to put on a play for Theseus and Hippolyta's wedding celebrations, and they need to rehearse.

Bottom is excited! He has the part of Pyramus, the lover who kills himself for love. He's sure he can make the audience cry:

'That will ask some tears in the true performing of it: if I do it, let the audience look to their eyes; I will move storms.'

But he really wants to play a tyrant. He says he would make a great Hercules.

Flute will play the part of Thisbe, the lady that Pyramus is in love with. Flute's not happy though: he can't play a lady, as he's growing a beard. Bottom says he's happy to play both Pyramus and Thisbe. He can do both! He can speak in a woman's voice.

But no, Quince is firm with him.

Starveling will play Thisbe's mother, and Snout will be Pyramus's father. Quince will be Thisbe's father and Snug will play the part of the lion.

Bottom's off again. He wants to play the lion too – he's really good at roaring. '*I will roar, that I will do any man's heart good to hear me; I will roar, that I will make the duke say, "Let him roar again, let him roar again."*'

'No, no!' Quince tells Bottom. 'You would roar so loudly that all the ladies would be scared and the duke would order us all to be hanged! *You can play no part but Pyramus; for Pyramus is a sweet-faced man; a proper man, as one shall see in a summer's day; a most lovely, gentleman-like man: therefore you must needs play Pyramus.*' Quince knows how to handle Bottom's enthusiasm.

'Oh! Oh!' Bottom has another thought. 'Can I wear a false beard? What colour? What colour?' He is like a big kid!

'We will meet in the palace wood tomorrow night to rehearse,' Quince tells them all. 'Nobody will bother us there. Now, don't let me down!'

TWO

We're in a wood, near Athens. **Puck** is standing there. (Puck also goes by the name of **Robin Goodfellow**.) He is a clever little elf, or sprite, and he is a servant of **Oberon**, the King of the Fairies. Puck is talking to a **fairy**, a servant of the Fairy Queen, **Titania**.

Puck tells the fairy that Titania and Oberon have had a massive row. Titania has kidnapped a boy child from the humans and she wants him to be her servant. But jealous Oberon wants the boy too; he wants him to be a knight in his service. Oberon is furious, but Titania won't give him up. Now, whenever they meet, they argue – and everyone has to creep into acorn cups to hide!

The fairy narrows her eyes. 'I know you – you are that *shrewd and knavish sprite*

Call'd Robin Goodfellow. You play nasty little tricks, like scaring the maidens in the village, stealing the cream from the top of the milk, stopping the milk turning to butter, or getting weary travellers really lost. You even make the beer go flat.'

'*Thou speak'st aright,*' Puck laughs. '*I am that merry wanderer of the night.*

I jest to Oberon and make him smile. I make old ladies spill their drink down their fronts. I pretend to be a stool and then disappear, so some old lady falls down on her bum. Ha ha! But watch out!' adds Puck. 'Here comes King Oberon.'

'And here's my mistress, Titania.'

Sure enough, King Oberon appears, surrounded by his followers, and at the same

time Queen Titania enters, surrounded by
her followers. Oberon sees Titania. Titania
sees Oberon.

'*Ill met by moonlight, proud Titania,*'
Oberon spits.

'Fairies, run for it,' shrieks Titania. 'I've
sworn I'll never sleep in his bed or talk to
him again.'

'Hang on!' says Oberon. '*Am not I thy
lord?* Aren't you supposed to obey me?'

'And you're supposed to be faithful to me.

But I know you've been sneaking away from Fairy Land to sing love songs to your new girlfriend. And you're only here because *the bouncing Amazon* [she means Hippolyta] is getting married to Theseus!' Titania yells.

'And I know you love Theseus!' Oberon shouts back.

'These are just jealous lies,' Titania says. 'We poor fairies get no peace to do our jobs any more, because of you and your arguments. The winds are upset and the rivers overflow. The fields are under water and the crops are rotting. The air carries disease and now winter is coming in the middle of summer. Everything is spoiled and it's all because of our arguing. It's our fault.'

'Put it right, then,' says Oberon. 'Give me the boy.'

'No,' answers Titania. 'The boy's mother was a worshipper of mine and she died giving birth to him. *For her sake I will not part with him.*' Then Titania storms off, followed by her fairies.

Oberon vows to pay Titania back for her insult. He calls Puck over.

'Puck, come here. Do you remember that time we saw a mermaid riding on a dolphin's back? She was singing, remember? The same night, I saw Cupid shoot a dart at a beautiful virgin. He missed, but the arrow fell on a little flower called love-in-idleness. If you can find that flower, I can make a magic juice from it. I know that if I put that juice on a man or a woman's eyes when they are asleep, then when they wake up they will fall in love with the first living thing they see. Go fetch me that flower and bring it here.'

'I'll get it now,' Puck answers. 'I can go around the whole world in 40 minutes!' He whizzes off.

Oberon plans to put the juice on Titania's eyes as she sleeps.

'The next thing then she waking looks upon,
Be it on lion, bear, or wolf, or bull,
On meddling monkey, or on busy ape,

She shall pursue it with the soul of love.'
Oberon has an antidote to the potion, but guess what? She will only get it if she gives up the boy first. 'Serves her right!' he thinks.

Suddenly Oberon hears some people coming. He decides to make himself invisible and listen in on their conversation.

Enter Demetrius and Helena, unaware that Oberon is watching and listening.

Helena is following Demetrius, who's not happy. *'I love thee not, therefore pursue me not,'* Demetrius tells Helena. 'Where are Hermia and Lysander? I want to see Hermia!'

But Helena won't be put off. 'I can't help it,' she says to Demetrius.

'I am your spaniel; and, Demetrius,
The more you beat me, I will fawn on you:
Use me but as your spaniel, spurn me, strike me,
Neglect me, lose me; only give me leave,
Unworthy as I am, to follow you.'

Poor Helena. She's got it bad.

Demetrius is blunt: '*For I am sick when I do look on thee,*' he tells Helena. Ouch!

'*And I am sick when I look not on you,*' she replies. Straight back at you.

'I swear, Helena, I'm going to run away and leave you with the wild animals. Now leave me alone, or I'll do something bad to you in the woods.'

'It would be heavenly to be killed by somebody I love so much,' she tells him.

Demetrius leaves – followed by Helena.

Oberon has been watching quietly. That poor girl! He decides he will use any left-over love juice to make Demetrius love Helena.

Then, *Ziiippp!* Puck is back, and he has the love-in-idleness flower, as Oberon asked.

'Give it to me!' says Oberon. 'I know where Titania sleeps, on a grassy bank overgrown with flowers. There she snores amongst the violets, wild herbs and roses. I will put some of this juice on her eyes
And make her full of hateful fantasies.'

Oberon has another job for Puck. 'Now, Puck, in this forest a sweet Athenian lady is in love with a young man, but he wants nothing to do with her. Put some of this flower's juice on his eyes, and make sure that the next thing he sees will be the lady. You'll be able to tell it's him because he's wearing city clothes from Athens. Then make sure you meet me before dawn.'

'I'm your sprite!' Puck says proudly, and off he goes.

Titania and her fairies are asleep in the forest. As they sleep, Oberon sneaks up to them and puts a few drops of the flower's juice on Titania's eyelids. When she wakes up, she will fall in love with the first living thing she sees.

Oberon then leaves … just as Lysander and Hermia enter. They have been wandering in the forest and both are tired and lost, so they decide to lay down in the wood to sleep for a bit. Lysander wants them to cuddle up, but Hermia tells him, 'No cuddling until we are married.' So they lie down and quickly fall asleep.

And that is where Puck finds them both. He's had no luck finding the couple Oberon asked him to look for ... but now here they are! Puck looks at Lysander, dressed in his smart Athenian city clothes, and decides that he must be the person Oberon meant. So Puck puts some flower juice on Lysander's eyelids, and then he departs.

Now it's time for the plot to thicken. As Lysander and Hermia sleep, enter Demetrius, closely followed by (guess who?) Helena. Demetrius leaves, but Helena stays ... and spots Lysander. She decides to wake him up, to check that he's OK.

So Lysander wakes and sees Helena. Helena! Suddenly he is madly in love with her.

'Helena,' he says, 'in your eyes I see the true story of love.'

Helena is angry. 'Lysander, do not make fun of me. You love Hermia, and Hermia loves you. You must be content.'

'Content with Hermia! No; I do repent
The tedious minutes I with her have spent.
Not Hermia but Helena I love:
Who will not change a raven for a dove?'

That flower juice definitely works!

Then Helena leaves, closely followed by Lysander.

Later, Hermia wakes up, rubbing her eyes from a bad dream she'd been having. She'd dreamt a snake had eaten her heart away. She looks around – and sees that her lover Lysander has gone (in more ways than one).

'Either death or you I'll find immediately,' she says, as she starts to look for him.

THREE

We're still in the forest, next to Titania and her sleeping fairies. The workmen are all gathering there too, as it's just where they agreed to meet to rehearse the play.

They are talking about the play. Bottom has some worries. What if the ladies are scared when Bottom's character Pyramus stabs himself? Bottom thinks he must have a speech telling them it is all just pretend.

Snout worries that the ladies might also be scared of the lion. He needs a speech too, to tell everybody it's not a real lion.

Peter Quince worries that they need

moonlight, because Pyramus and Thisbe meet by moonlight.

Oh, and what about the wall the two lovers, Pyramus and Thisbe, talk through? That is a real problem. But Bottom has an idea! One of them should play the part of the wall, and hold up his fingers to make the hole in the wall!

All sorted! It will be just like a real play!

As they rehearse, Puck turns up, unseen, and watches them.

Bottom says all his lines at once, not waiting for the other players to say theirs. He gets his words wrong, too, telling Thisbe she is '*odious*' instead of '*odorous*'.

Poor Peter Quince is pulling his hair out.

Puck, on a wicked impulse, grabs poor Nick Bottom and uses magic to turn his head into an ass's head. The workmen are all terrified and run away.

Bottom thinks they are playing a trick on him: '*I see their knavery: this is to make an ass of me; to fright me, if they could.*' He decides to walk up and down, singing loudly, to show that he is not afraid.

Well, all this loud singing and walking around wakes up Titania, who takes one look at the donkey-headed person in front of her … and falls instantly in love.

'*What angel wakes me from my flowery bed?*' she asks. Then she tells Bottom that she is in love with him.

'You've got little reason to love me,'

replies Bottom, 'although reason and love don't have much to do with each other these days.'

'*Thou art as wise as thou art beautiful,*' Titania replies. (Well, she got that bit right.)

'I just wish I was wise enough to get out of this wood!'

Titania is horrified. Bottom is going nowhere. 'Oh no. *Thou shalt remain here, whether thou wilt or no.*'

She orders her fairies to look after Bottom and fetch him '*jewels from the deep.*' He isn't going anywhere soon!

Meanwhile, Oberon is waiting for news. Has Titania woken up? Has she fallen in love yet? Puck arrives and is extremely pleased to tell Oberon what happened, in all its details. He ends with:

'*When in that moment, so it came to pass,*
Titania waked and straightway loved an ass.'

'This is going better than I expected,' says Oberon. 'Did you sort the two Athenians as I asked?' he adds.

'I did,' Puck boasts. 'I found him sleeping and gave him a good squirt.'

Just as he says that, Demetrius and Hermia enter.

'Ah, that's him,' says Oberon, 'but now he's with a different girl.'

'No,' replies Puck. 'That's the same girl, but it's a different man. Oops!'

Demetrius thinks Hermia is drop-dead gorgeous – so why is she so nasty to him? But Hermia is still trying to find her love, Lysander.

'If you have hurt Lysander … ' she says. Has her lover been murdered by Demetrius?

'He is still alive,' says Demetrius.

'Don't talk to me! I'm going – and you'll never see me again, whether Lysander is dead or not.' Hermia leaves.

Demetrius lies down and closes his eyes in despair. Soon he is asleep.

Oberon looks at Puck in amazement. *'What hast thou done?* Who did you drug? You should have made a false love true, but it looks as though you've made a true love bad.'

'Well it's OK, it's just fate,' replies Puck. 'It's the way of the world.'

Oberon isn't happy. They need to put things right. 'Find Helena and bring her to me. I'll do the eyelids of this one here,' (he's looking at sleeping Demetrius), 'ready for her. We need to sort all this out!'

Demetrius has had the eyelid treatment and Puck has returned, bringing Lysander (who is now in love with Helena) and Helena (who is still in love with Demetrius) back to where Demetrius (who did love Helena, and then loved Hermia, but will soon love Helena again – as soon as he wakes up) is sleeping. (Do you need to draw a chart? It's tricky keeping up!)

Lysander has already told Helena he is in

love with her, but she thinks he is winding her up. '*You do advance your cunning more and more,*' she tells him. 'You told Hermia you loved her, and now you say the same to me. They're both lies.'

'Look,' Lysander says, '*Demetrius loves her, and he loves not you.*'

At that moment, Demetrius wakes up and sees Helena. The flower juice does its work. '*O Helena, goddess, nymph, perfect, divine!* Your lips are *kissing cherries.* Oh, oh, let me kiss you!'

Helena's not convinced. First Lysander says he loves her, and now Demetrius.

'*O spite! O hell! I see you all are bent*

To set against me for your merriment.

I know you both hate me; isn't that enough? Why do you have to mock me as well? I know you both love Hermia.'

Lysander tells Demetrius he can have Hermia; Lysander doesn't want her any more. He just wants Helena.

'*Lysander, keep thy Hermia; I will none,*'

replies Demetrius. 'If I ever loved her, that love is all gone. My heart has now returned home to Helena, and there it will remain.'

Helena watches in confusion. '*Never did mockers waste more idle breath,*' she says to herself.

Then in the midst of all this, Hermia turns up.

Straight away, she sees Lysander.

'Why did you leave me, Lysander?' she asks.
'Love told me to go,' he replies.

'But what love could make you leave me?' Hermia asks him.

'My love for fair Helena and the fact I hate you.'

Ouch!

Hermia is astonished. *'You speak not as you think: it cannot be.'*

To add to the confusion, Helena thinks that Hermia is joining in the joke against her. 'Hermia, how can you do this to me? We have always been best friends. Do you want to destroy our friendship, just to join with these two men and mock me?'

Hermia of course is now even more confused. *'I scorn you not: it seems that you scorn me …*

I understand not what you mean by this,' she tells Helena.

Helena has one more try:

'If you have any pity, grace, or manners,
You would not make me such an argument.
But fare ye well: 'tis partly my own fault;
Which death or absence soon shall remedy.'

Lysander puts out his arms to his beloved Helena. 'Helena, stay, I love you!'

Demetrius cries out, '*I say I love thee more than he can do.*'

Lysander then challenges Demetrius to a duel (which hardly seems to be the best way to sort out these kinds of things). Demetrius agrees.

Hermia tries to hold onto Lysander, but he pushes her away and shakes her off:

'*Hang off, thou cat, thou burr! vile thing, let loose,*

Or I will shake thee from me like a serpent!'

Slowly Hermia realises what has happened. Somehow Helena has stolen her Lysander. '*You juggler! you canker-blossom! You thief of love!* How have you stolen him?'

Helena is straight back at her: '*Fie, fie! you counterfeit, you puppet, you!*'

Puppet? Hermia thinks that because Helena is tall and she is short, Helena is insulting her by calling her a puppet.

'*How low am I, thou painted maypole? speak;*

How low am I? I am not yet so low
But that my nails can reach unto thine eyes.'

'Don't let her hurt me!' Helena says to
Demetrius and Lysander. 'Hermia, I've
never done anything to hurt you – except
when I told Demetrius that you and
Lysander were both going to meet secretly
in this wood. Now, just leave me and let me
go quietly back to Athens.'

'Let me at her!' Hermia is furious at
being called 'little'.

Lysander knows whose side he's on! He
turns to Hermia:

'Get you gone, you dwarf;
You minimus, of hindering knot-grass made;
You bead, you acorn.' (Lysander *is* good at
coming up with insults, you have to admit.)

Then Lysander turns to Demetrius. 'I'll
fight you for Helena, Demetrius!' They rush
off to find a good place for a duel.

Hermia and Helena both leave too –
heading in different directions.

All this time, Oberon and Puck have been watching the events unfold, unseen of course. Oberon is even more unhappy.

'This is all your fault,' he says to Puck. 'You make mistakes all the time – or else you do it on purpose.'

'It was a mistake,' says Puck. 'I did just what you asked – I put the flower juice on an Athenian's eyes. And I must say, so far it's all been very entertaining.'

But Oberon wants it all sorted. 'No! We need to sort all this out! Puck, make the night dark and add a dark fog, so these *testy rivals* [Demetrius and Lysander] get lost and can't find each other. Then tire them out trying to find each other, so that they sleep like the dead.'

Oberon gives Puck another flower potion, an antidote to the first potion. 'Then crush this potion in Lysander's eyes, and
*When they next wake, all this derision
Shall seem a dream and fruitless vision.*'

Then they will all go back to Athens, Oberon tells Puck, and all will be well.

'Meanwhile,' Oberon continues, 'I will go and find Titania and ask her once again for the boy. Then I will give her this potion and undo the spell on her. Then *all things shall be peace.*'

So Puck begins his task.

Pretending to be Lysander and then

Demetrius, he lures both men to the same spot in the forest and then manages to get them both asleep.

As Puck stands, invisible, over the sleeping men, Helena enters. She too is tired, after such a *'long and tedious night'*, and she too lies down and falls asleep.

Puck has three of them; now he just needs number four.

Sure enough, enter Hermia. She too is tired, and (guess what) she too lies down and falls asleep.

Quickly Puck adds a few drops of the second flower juice onto Lysander's eyes.

'In your waking shall be shown:

Jack shall have Jill;

Nought shall go ill;

The man shall have his mare again, and all shall be well.'

FOUR

We're still in the forest, with Lysander, Demetrius, Helena and Hermia all asleep. As they sleep, Bottom, Titania and her fairies enter. Bottom, of course, still has the head of an ass that Puck gave him. Oberon stands in the background, unseen and watching everything.

It's now the day of Theseus and Hippolyta's wedding, and Bottom's having a great time. The fairies have looked after him well, and even scratched his head for him. Now the fairies depart, leaving him 'alone' with Titania.

'O, *how I love thee! how I dote on thee!*'
Titania sighs, as she and Bottom fall asleep.

As they sleep, Puck enters and is greeted by Oberon. Oberon tells Puck that he feels guilty about what he did to Titania. She has already agreed to give him the stolen boy, so he says he will give her the second potion straight away:

'*And now I have the boy, I will undo*
This hateful imperfection of her eyes.'

So Titania wakes, no longer under the spell of the flower juice.

'*My Oberon! what visions have I seen!*
Methought I was enamour'd of an ass.'

A bit red-faced, Oberon points to Bottom (still asleep, with his ass's head). 'That one?'

'O, *how mine eyes do loathe his visage now!*'

Oberon then gets Puck to use his magic to remove the ass's head from the still-sleeping Bottom, returning him to his original human form.

'Come on,' Oberon says to Titania, 'we

are friends again now. Let's go to Duke Theseus' wedding and see all the pairs of lovers properly married, each to the right person.'

As they all leave, Titania is thinking, 'Yes, and on the way you can explain to me exactly how I ended up sleeping on the ground with all these humans.'

Theseus and Hippolyta are out hunting in the forest with Egeus, when they come across the four sleeping characters. (They don't notice Bottom.)

Of course they know immediately who they all are, and they wake them up.

Lysander is dazed and sleepy. 'I don't remember how I got here at all. I think I came here with Hermia. We were planning to escape Athenian law … '

Egeus is furious. 'Arrest him!'

Demetrius is still sleepy too. 'No, don't do that! Helena told me Lysander and Hermia were coming here, so I followed them. And Helena followed me.'

Demetrius has more news: he no longer loves Hermia. (Remember, he is still under the spell of the first potion.)

'*But by some power it is – my love to Hermia,*
Melted as the snow …
The object and the pleasure of mine eye,
Is only Helena.'

'Right!' Theseus says. He's had enough of all this. 'I'm overruling you, Egeus. Lysander will marry Hermia. Demetrius will marry Helena. And they'll do it today, in Athens, at the same time that Hippolyta and I get married! End of! Get over it!'

Theseus, Hippolyta and Egeus head back to Athens, leaving four bewildered people behind.

Demetrius asks, *'Are you sure*
That we are awake? It seems to me
That yet we sleep, we dream.'

Demetrius, Lysander, Helena and Hermia all head back to Athens, agreeing to recount their strange dreams to each other as they go.

As they leave, Bottom wakes up. 'I have had such a strange dream. It was … no, I can't say it. Instead I will get Peter Quince to write a song about it, and call it "Bottom's Dream." '

He rushes off to get the other players ready. They can't do without their Bottom!

FIVE

Back in Athens, at Theseus's palace, the weddings have taken place and all three couples are now married. Theseus and Hippolyta are discussing the recent strange events. Hippolyta is puzzled. 'It's a strange story, isn't it? Falling in love, falling out of love. And they are all saying the same thing. I don't think it was a dream.'

Theseus is not so sure:

'*More strange than true: I never may believe*
These antique fables, nor these fairy toys.'

Then Demetrius, Lysander, Helena and Hermia turn up. Everybody is going to have a great evening together. As entertainment, Theseus insists on hearing Peter Quince's play. Philostrate tells him that it is terrible, but Theseus chooses to see it anyway, because the workmen mean well.

So the play is performed in front of the audience of newly-weds. It's not a great performance; in fact it proves hard to hold the laughter in.

Snout, as the Wall, is the highlight. Covered in mud, he explains,

'I am a wall. This circle I am making with my fingers is a hole in the wall for the lovers to whisper through.'

Demetrius says it is the cleverest wall he has ever heard! At the end of the scene, the wall and the two lovers, Pyramus and Thisbe, troop off together in their big workman boots.

'*This is the silliest stuff that ever I heard,*' Hippolyta giggles.

'Plays are all pretending. You just need a lot of imagination!' laughs Theseus.

The lion and the moon are on next, and they both carefully explain that they are not really a lion or a moon. 'Go on, Moon,' Lysander says, 'go for it!'

Finally it is Bottom's big scene. As the lover, Pyramus, he has to die. He gives it all he's got:

Thus die I, thus, thus, thus.
Now am I dead,
Now am I fled;
My soul is in the sky …
Now die, die, die, die, die.'

Thisbe stomps back on and, finding Pyramus dead, kills herself out of sorrow.

'Would you like to see the epilogue now?' Bottom asks.

'No,' Theseus says quickly. 'Your play doesn't need anything else. All the actors are dead, so nobody needs to be blamed in an epilogue.'

So the actors dance instead.

Finally it is past midnight. '*Lovers, to bed;* *'tis almost fairy time*,' declares Theseus.

So six lovers lie in bed, each with the right person, and as they sleep they are visited by the fairies. Titania looks on as Oberon gives them a special blessing. 'May their children all be beautiful and lucky and may the lovers be true. Bless this palace with sweet peace.'

Puck has the last word. Speaking to the audience, he says, 'If we actors have offended you in this play, just think that you were asleep here, and these were all just visions in a dream. I'm an honest Puck, and I will make everything up to you. If not, then I'm a liar.'

And off he flies.

 **THE END**

What's the play about?

This unusual, dream-like play is a comedy. It is about love, magic and power struggles. Love is confusing (and causes confusion), but love ultimately conquers all – with a little bit of help from the fairies!

* The play is about how love makes us act, including how hurtful we can be.

* It's about how life is full of strange coincidences.

* In the play, everything that is normal is turned around, and the world is made topsy-turvy. A character may love one person, but then they change their affections to another in a moment.

*   The play is about how power, however great, won't always win against what is right.

*   Finally, the play seems to show us that reality is not the hard and fast thing we often think it to be. Here, dreams and reality merge and blur, making characters unsure about what is real and what is not.

What are the main themes in the play?

Love – Love seems to be a major theme in this play, but this is not a love story. The emotions of the characters who are in love are never really explored. Rather, the theme is the difficulty of love, and the (amusing) troubles the characters get into because of love.

At the end of the play, it seems that Demetrius only loves Helena (rather than Hermia) because of Oberon's flower juice. That is not how 'love stories' end!

Magic and the supernatural – Do fairies and magic really exist? Do they have any control over our lives? Or do we alone decide what happens to us? Oberon and Puck use magic in the play to cause chaos and (at the end) to restore balance. Puck is also happy to use magic for his own fun.

Opposites – Shakespeare fills the play with opposites: Helena is tall, Hermia is short; Titania is beautiful, Bottom is ugly; the fairies are elegant and magical, the workmen are rough and ready.

Power over people – In Shakespeare's time, women belonged to their fathers until marriage, then they belonged to their husbands. Hermia tries to disobey her father, forcing him to ask Theseus, the most powerful man in Athens, to step in. Titania and Oberon are fighting for control of a human child, which strains their relationship.

Dream and reality – The play successfully merges dream and reality. Many characters wake up not sure if what they remember was a dream or whether it really happened.

Shakespeare's words

A *Midsummer Night's Dream* is a comedy, and Shakespeare uses language throughout to reinforce this, as well as to make us laugh.

Shakespeare uses **rhythm and rhyme** to distinguish between the characters.

* The graceful, elegant fairies speak in rhyme throughout the play, whilst the rough workmen, for example, speak in ordinary prose, just as we do.

   The only exception to this is when the workmen are performing their play, *Pyramus and Thisbe*. In their performance they too speak in rhyme, but it is very bad rhyme, adding to the humour.

There are many entertaining **insults** in this play, which are very inventive.

✳ At one point Lysander says to Hermia:

Get you gone, you dwarf;

You minimus, of hindering knot-grass made;

You bead, you acorn.

We know Hermia is short; Lysander calls her a dwarf (insulting enough), but also hindering knot-grass. Knot-grass was a weed that was supposed to stunt a person's growth.

Shakespeare uses other **strong images** too.

✳ When Hermia is upset at her father's objections to her marrying Lysander, Lysander tells her:

The course of true love never did run smooth.

He is putting the image in our minds of love being like a river; there may be obstacles along the way but, like a river, true love cannot be stopped.